MW00901806
I'm Happy
I'm me...
a Girl!
Donna R. Styer
Illustrated by Deborah Taylor

Author's Dedication:

To my granddaughters with great love:

Courtney, Kaila, Kara, Kirstin,

Nicole, Kyleigh, Laila and Lilly

May you forever treasure true self...

Illustrator's Dedication:

Lovingly dedicated to my mom,

who taught me that I can do anything,

and to all my girls

who embody her spirit.

Philippians 4:13

To Parents and Caregivers:

I'm Happy I'm Me... A Girl! is a little book with a very BIG message!

"I can..." is the perfect phrase to teach children aged 6 months through 1st grade.

Use each page for additional teaching opportunities:

- Counting
- Colors
- Rhyming
- Nature
- Diversity
- Physical activities

The girls and women I met throughout my life have helped me to understand that the messages we hear from a very young age are *extremely* important for our adult years!

And just for fun... find a firefly hidden on almost every page.

Illustrator's Note

Through the centuries, rhymes have proven invaluable in early childhood development. Beyond language skills, improved reading comprehension and building memory, rhymes enhance relationships, foster curiosity, develop an ear for rhythm and music, and expand the imagination.

This sparkling rhyme for little girls invites you to a grand adventure, stirred by the virtues and values that serve, shape, and strengthen women.

The images are filled with wonder and appreciation of the universe. You are encouraged to talk about the changing of the seasons, the moon, the sun, and the stars… as well as the beauty of nature including fireflies, cattails, the Red Buckeye tree, and the flamingo's nest. These discussions prepare the soil of our human souls and plant the seeds of stewardship and conservation.

No matter the age, a girl's indomitable spirit comes to life in these pages. A girl can do anything!

I'm a girl!

I can
do anything.

I can...
paint the house,
...or catch a mouse.

I can...
hop on one leg,

...or lay like an egg.

kiss a frog,

...or roll like a log.

I can...
jog for a mile,
...or give a big smile.

I can...
fly a kite

...or make a fist real tight.

I can...

hit a ball
with my head,

...or hide under the bed.

I can…
climb high up a tree,

...or even catch a bee.

I can... **row a boat,**

...or even float.

I can...

get angry and scream,

…or catch a moonbeam.

I can...

play in the rain,

...or drive a huge train.

I can...
pat a pig,

...and do a jig.

I can...
travel to
the moon,

...and be back by noon.

Yes...

A girl can do anything!

I'm happy

I'm me!

____

My Name

About the Author

DONNA R. STYER's enthusiasm for transforming businesses and individuals has made her a successful executive, career and life coach, and management consultant for over twenty-five years.

A former preschool teacher, the lessons she taught about tackling obstacles and learning to work well with others are equally relevant for children and adults.

She resides in central Pennsylvania, and is the founder and CEO of D.R. Styer & Associates.

About the Illustrator

DEBORAH TAYLOR has illustrated for friends and family for over forty years. She draws her inspiration from her Creator and the gifts of her husband, children, and grandchildren.

An eager learner and adventurer, her interests are endless as she's known to pursue all things beautiful. She resides in Maryland with her husband but is often found globetrotting with paints in pocket.

Softcover ISBN: 978-1-64649-091-2 Hardcover ISBN: 978-1-64649-092-9

Made in the USA
Middletown, DE
16 October 2020